MORE Fun with WALDO

Based on the characters created by
MARTIN HANDFORD

Little, Brown and Company
Boston Toronto London

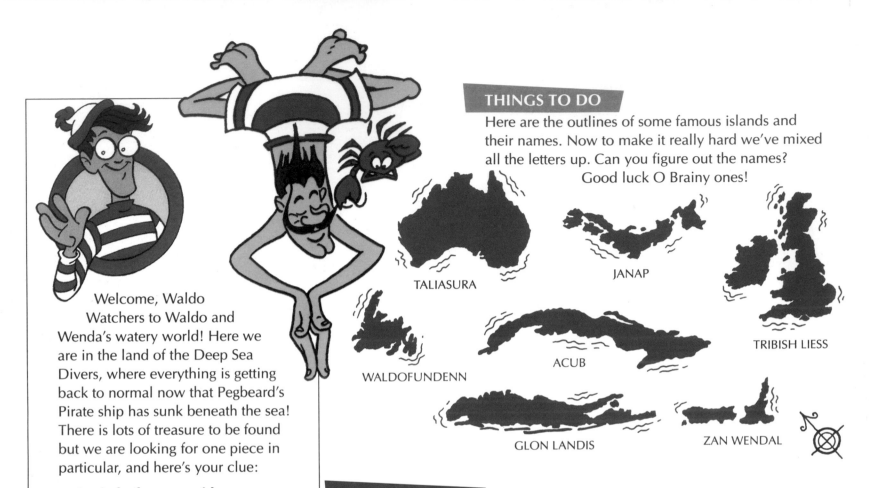

Welcome, Waldo Watchers to Waldo and Wenda's watery world! Here we are in the land of the Deep Sea Divers, where everything is getting back to normal now that Pegbeard's Pirate ship has sunk beneath the sea! There is lots of treasure to be found but we are looking for one piece in particular, and here's your clue:

Lucinda the mermaid,
Is waving at you.
Find her a jewel,
That's precious and blue.

While you're looking for Lucinda's gem can you spot our wishy-washy villain, Odlaw? He's already had his disguise discovered by someone!

THINGS TO DO

Here are the outlines of some famous islands and their names. Now to make it really hard we've mixed all the letters up. Can you figure out the names? Good luck O Brainy ones!

TALIASURA

JANAP

TRIBISH LIESS

WALDOFUNDENN

ACUB

GLON LANDIS

ZAN WENDAL

DID YOU KNOW?

The aqualung, a tank containing compressed air, was first developed by Jaques Cousteau and Emile Gagnan in 1943 for underwater exploration.

High divers from La Quebrada at Acapulco, Mexico dive into the water from cliffs 87½ feet high! The water is only 12 feet deep! Wow!

In 1989 Angela Bandini of Italy held her breath while diving down to 351 feet. She was underwater for 2 minutes 46 seconds, an extremely dangerous thing to do!

The Lutine Bell, which was salvaged from a wrecked British warship, hangs in the insurance office of Lloyds of London. It is rung each time a ship is reported missing or destroyed at sea.

Wow, there's nothing like having some fun while you dig, and the Mushroom Mining Trolls certainly know all about having fun. The Main Mushroom Mining Troll, who is wearing a medal, is not as happy as he could be:

**It's all work and no play,
That is plain to see.
Someone's taken his yo-yo,
Now where can it be?**

Who took it? Can you spot him? And who is the troll missing a light bulb from his hat? Meanwhile, I must get looking for Woof, I know he's around here somewhere!

Mushrooms are only one of more than 100,000 different types of fungi!

THINGS TO DO

Can you help Trumpeter Troll to collect four musical notes and reach the other members of the band?

DID YOU KNOW?

The first tunnel was built in 2160 BC by Queen Semiramis of Babylon! It went under the Euphrates river and was 3,000 feet long! Wow!

The ancient Egyptians used tunnels for both carrying water and as tombs!

A Mycologist is a man who studies fungi.

A toadstool and a mushroom are the same thing.

Unlike our happy Mushroom Miners a Troll in old Scandinavian stories was a horrible, nasty forest dweller with magical powers. Trolls weren't very bright, so they were nearly always outwitted!

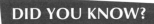

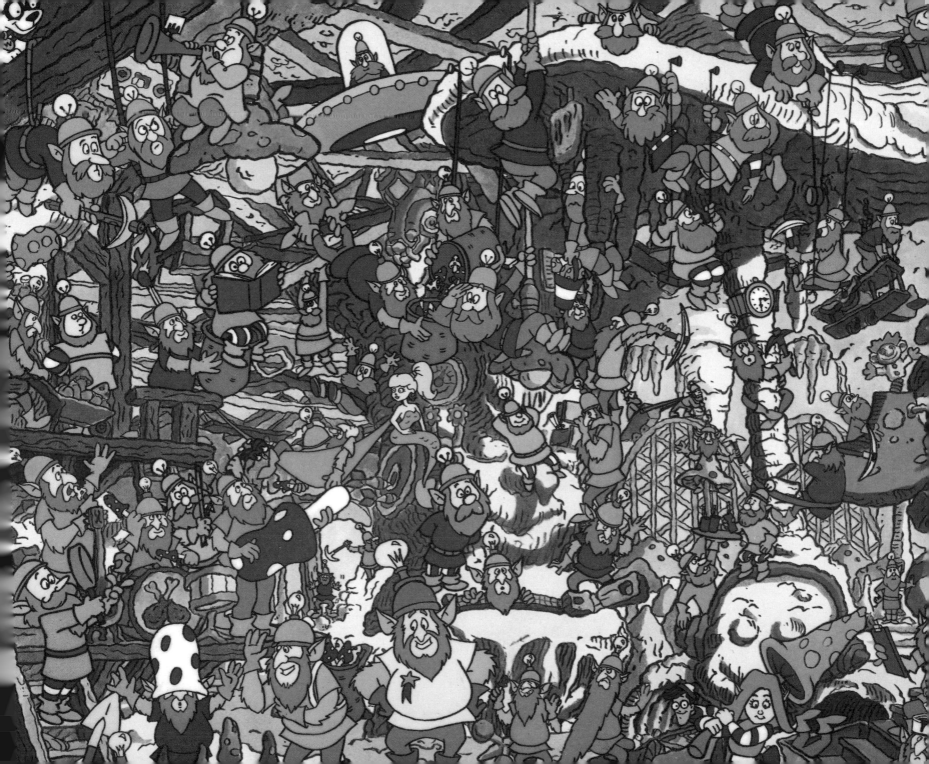

What fabulous, flying, fun! Even Whitebeard and Woof have joined in. Ali Blobi's henchmen are making a mess of this carpet mall. They are looking for Ali's carpet, which flew away to escape his terrible treatment - he hasn't vacuumed it once, Crumbs! Well, here's a clue to help you spot this messy mat:

**This rug's on the run,
From a dirty old stinker.
It's caught by a lady,
Hook, line, and sinker!**

There are two timepieces in the picture telling us that time is running out. Can you spot them in this rug rush?

THINGS TO DO

(a)

(b)

(c)

d)

(e)

(f)

Here are six heads of Blobi. Only two are identical. Can you tell which they are?

DID YOU KNOW?

In the 18th and 19th centuries old galleons were used as floating prisons called hulks.

One of the most famous prisoners was Napoleon Bonaparte, who was imprisoned on the island of Elba in 1814, but escaped after 100 days. After the battle of Waterloo, he was sent to another island, St Helena, where he eventually died.

Alcatraz means Pelican in Spanish. The old prison in San Francisco Bay is named Alcatraz because of the pelicans which fly around it.

There were only seven prisoners in the Bastille when the Paris Mob attacked it in 1789 to begin the French Revolution.

A Palindrome reads the same forwards as backwards.

Napoleon is supposed to have said: "Able was I ere I saw Elba" Another one is: "Madam, I'm Adam"

Can you think of any?

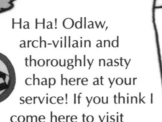

Ha Ha! Odlaw, arch-villain and thoroughly nasty chap here at your service! If you think I come here to visit some friends then you really don't know me very well! I'm looking for something which I've been told will make me incredibly rich! All I have is this riddle:

**I live nine times over,
Before I grow old,
With a coat that sparkles,
For it's made of gold.**

So if you can help me I promise to give you a huge prize and Odlaw never goes back on a promise - well, not since yesterday! Anyway, stop this lollygagging and get searching!

THINGS TO DO

·WANTED·
ODLAW'S HEROES

Odlaw's Outlaws - here are a few of my very favorite chaps. Each one has something stolen from the picture opposite - hee hee my heroes!! Can you spot what they have pinched?

(a)

(b) BONO

(c) THE KID

(d) JAKE 5

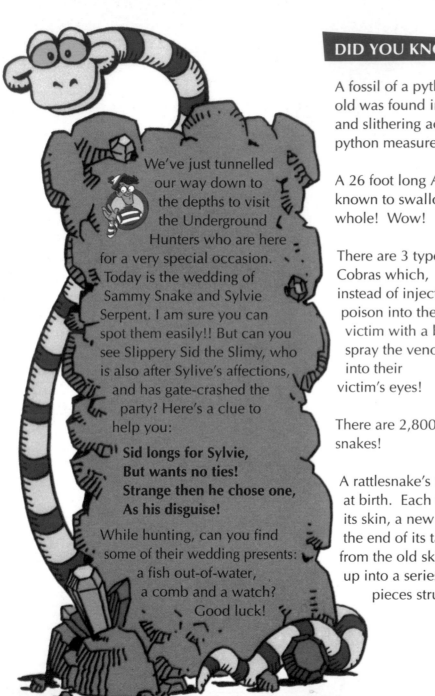

We've just tunnelled our way down to the depths to visit the Underground Hunters who are here for a very special occasion. Today is the wedding of Sammy Snake and Sylvie Serpent. I am sure you can spot them easily!! But can you see Slippery Sid the Slimy, who is also after Sylive's affections, and has gate-crashed the party? Here's a clue to help you:

**Sid longs for Sylvie,
But wants no ties!
Strange then he chose one,
As his disguise!**

While hunting, can you find some of their wedding presents: a fish out-of-water, a comb and a watch? Good luck!

DID YOU KNOW?

A fossil of a python 38 million years old was found in Egypt. When alive and slithering across the sands, the python measured 37 feet in length!

A 26 foot long Anaconda has been known to swallow a 100 lb pig whole! Wow!

There are 3 types of Cobras which, instead of injecting poison into their victim with a bite, spray the venom into their victim's eyes!

There are 2,800 different species of snakes!

A rattlesnake's rattle begins to grow at birth. Each time the snake sheds its skin, a new hard tip is formed at the end of its tail. The segments from the old skin remain, building up into a series of hard, hollow pieces strung together.

① ② ③

THINGS TO DO

Look at this mass of snakes and see if you can find which one is coming out of the basket.

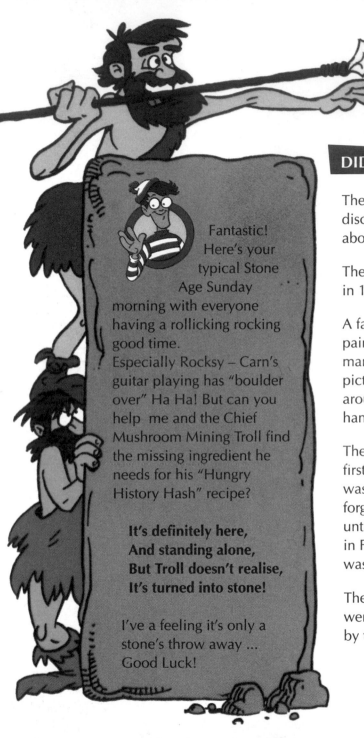

Fantastic! Here's your typical Stone Age Sunday morning with everyone having a rollicking rocking good time.
Especially Rocksy – Carn's guitar playing has "boulder over" Ha Ha! But can you help me and the Chief Mushroom Mining Troll find the missing ingredient he needs for his "Hungry History Hash" recipe?

**It's definitely here,
And standing alone,
But Troll doesn't realise,
It's turned into stone!**

I've a feeling it's only a stone's throw away ...
Good Luck!

DID YOU KNOW?

The first cave paintings weren't discovered until 1875. They are about 30,000 years old.

The first movie theater was built in 1895 in Atlanta, Georgia.

A favorite subject for cave painting was hunting. Stone Age man would sometimes "sign" his pictures by blowing pigment around his hand, leaving a handprint on the cave wall.

The man who discovered the first cave paintings, in Spain, was at first thought to have forged them. It was not until others were found in France that his name was cleared!

The most famous cave paintings were found at Lascaux in France by two boys out playing in 1940.

THINGS TO DO

Hidden in this stone tablet are the names of some of the things in the picture. Can you find them all?
Good Luck!

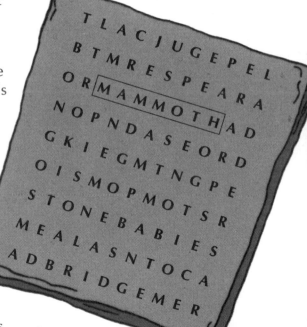

```
T L A C J U G E P E L
B T M R E S P E A R A
O R M A M M O T H A D
N O P N D A S E O R D
G K I E G M T N G P E
O I S M O P M O T S R
S T O N E B A B I E S
M E A L A S N T O C A
A D B R I D G E M E R
```

Figuring out the rules of the Great Ball game is always a lot of fun, O fanatical fans of Waldo. But, one thing you must remember, the rules change every few minutes and sometimes there are no rules at all! See if you can spot the captains of the two teams with the help of this clue:

**Captain Bart
Has a broken heart,
Captain Lou
Hides a ball from you.**

To figure out the score, count all the white balls and balloons for Bart's Hoods, and all the players with green uniforms for Lou's Shorts.

THINGS TO DO

Here's a drawing of a special sports man. How many sports do you think he can play?

DID YOU KNOW?

The oldest set of marbles ever found were in the grave of an Egyptian child dated 3,000 BC. The marbles were rounded semi-precious stones.

A game called "Tsu Chu," which means "to kick a ball of stuffed leather," was played in China more than 2,500 years ago!

A game very similar to basketball called "Pok-ta-Pok" was played in the 10th century BC by the Olmecs in Mexico!

The first ever winner of an Olympic event was Coroibos, a cook who won a foot race in 776 BC!

Look at this O wide-eyed, watchful, Waldo-Watchers! The Vikings have got inside the village but the villagers don't seem to mind. Maybe it's because Bunhilde's singing will make sure they don't stay around too long! Or, maybe it's because they can't find the treasure until they solve this riddle. See if you can solve this riddle and find the treasure before they do:

Although really gold,
It has been painted black.
If I tell you it's numbered,
This riddle you'll crack!

There again perhaps it's just because the Viking leader, Lars, has got himself stuck in a barrel and is thinking of giving up pillaging and taking up "villaging!"

DID YOU KNOW?

The Vikings founded many cities all over Europe and the Far East, including Dublin, the capital of Ireland.

The word "Vikings" means pirates!

Leif Eriksson, the Viking, landed in North America and established a colony there called Vinland, 500 years before Columbus.

Viking boats were called "Long Ships" and could be over 80 feet in length.

Only some Vikings were pirates. Most were wonderfully efficient farmers.

A tax called the Danegeld was levied in England to pay the Vikings so that they would not invade.

Unlike the characters in our picture, the real Vikings never had horns on their helmets.

THINGS TO DO

Look carefully at all of these shadows and see if you can match them to the people and objects in the picture. But, be careful, one of them is back-to-front!

DID YOU KNOW?

The Aztecs used no iron, not even for tools or weapons, and they did not have the wheel!

The Aztecs capital was called Tenochtitlan and was built in the marshes of Lake Tezcuco. This is now the site of Mexico City.

There were about 5 million Aztecs in 1519 - when the conquest by the Spanish began.

The Aztecs took their ball games seriously. Sometimes the captain of the losing team would have his head cut off.

Don't mix up the Aztecs (who lived in central Mexico) with the Incas, who lived along the Pacific coast of South America in parts of what are now Ecuador, Peru, and Chile.

The Aztecs were only one of three civilizations living in Mexico between 900 and 1500 AD. The others were the Mayans and the Toltecs.

Well, world-wide followers of Waldo, as you can see, I have been here before with Wenda. We left behind a pair of glasses, an umbrella, and one of our hats. Can you spot them? But more importantly, can you help warn the Aztecs of approaching danger?

**There's a spy in the village,
In disguise it is said.
Not wearing a helmet,
But a flag on his head!**

Can you spot the spy and the helmet he normally wears? See if you can guess why the Aztecs are in danger by reading the facts on this page. In the meantime perhaps the powers of the Phantom Avenger can help save the Villagers! He's the one wearing a mask.

THINGS TO DO

This Aztec temple has been destroyed in a terrible earthquake. Can you count how many blocks of stone the Aztecs would need to put their temple back together after a terrible earthquake?

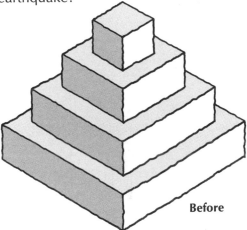

Before

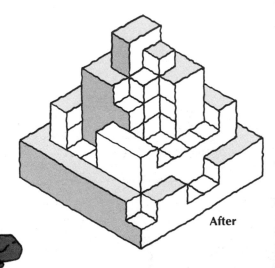

After

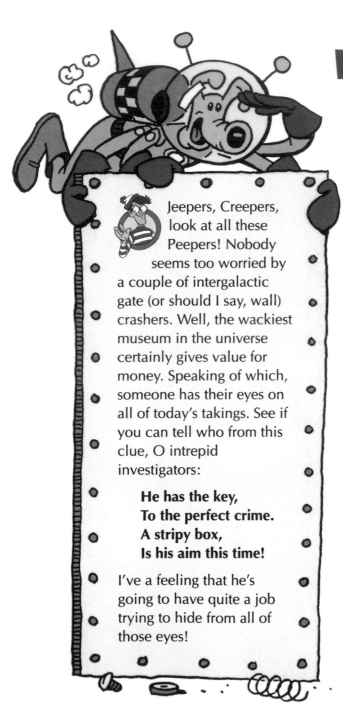

Jeepers, Creepers, look at all these Peepers! Nobody seems too worried by a couple of intergalactic gate (or should I say, wall) crashers. Well, the wackiest museum in the universe certainly gives value for money. Speaking of which, someone has their eyes on all of today's takings. See if you can tell who from this clue, O intrepid investigators:

**He has the key,
To the perfect crime.
A stripy box,
Is his aim this time!**

I've a feeling that he's going to have quite a job trying to hide from all of those eyes!

DID YOU KNOW?

The word "robot" was first used in a play called "R.U.R." written in 1921 by Karel Capek.

The Volkswagen "Beetle" or "Bug" has sold more than any other car. Its looks have changed very little since it was first designed in 1934.

Washing machines were first sold in 1832, but the first electrically powered machines did not appear until 1914.

The movie which has made the most money, is "E.T. the Extra Terrestrial" which has grossed over $700 million!

2 other movies based on space travel are also among the most popular films ever made:
"Star Wars" and "Close Encounters of the Third Kind".

THINGS TO DO

Get tongue untwisting double quick, if you dare, for even more fun!

Seventy-six saucy spaceships soar the southern solar system!
Modern martians must admire millions and millions of museum masterpieces from the past-a-pieces!

Wham-bam Wallop! Watch out Waldo! There's a crashing craft of cretinous cryptons careering carelessly into the collector's classic collection!

The Many Moons Museum makes many-a-minutes magical musing!

Now see if you can untwist these letters which will have become mixed up in all the madcap museum mayhem! They should each spell the name of a planet in our Solar System:

TOPUL   ASTURN

RETIPUJ   CURRYME

CHECK LISTS

FLYING CARPETS

- [ ] A Skateboard
- [ ] A Golf club
- [ ] A Man rolled in a carpet
- [ ] A Man wearing a scarf
- [ ] An Hour glass
- [ ] An Alarm clock
- [ ] A Crashed carpet
- [ ] A Lady sleeping
- [ ] 2 Men arguing
- [ ] A Carpet with a hole in it
- [ ] A Telescope
- [ ] An Urn with stars
- [ ] A Man reading a book

DUNGEON

- [ ] 2 Mousetraps
- [ ] A Television set
- [ ] A Fork and spoon
- [ ] A Blindfolded prisoner
- [ ] A Balloon and chain
- [ ] A Squirting fish
- [ ] A Soda
- [ ] A Maid
- [ ] A Basketball
- [ ] A Painting
- [ ] A Waiter
- [ ] A Beard in irons

DEEP SEA DIVERS

- [ ] 2 Dancing fish
- [ ] 2 Flying fish
- [ ] A Heart
- [ ] A Swordfish
- [ ] A Sawfish
- [ ] 4 Diving helmets
- [ ] A Golden anchor
- [ ] 2 Fish playing cards
- [ ] A Climbing eel
- [ ] A Boot
- [ ] A Fork and spoon
- [ ] A Ruby ring
- [ ] A Pirate octopus
- [ ] A Polka dot starfish
- [ ] A Salt shaker
- [ ] A Periscope

TROLLS

- [ ] A Biplane
- [ ] A Wristwatch
- [ ] A Flying saucer
- [ ] A Troll trapped in a zipper
- [ ] A Magnifying glass
- [ ] 2 Trolls wearing mushrooms
- [ ] A Cassette tape
- [ ] A Striped bucket
- [ ] A Lighted match
- [ ] A Jack-in-the-mushroom
- [ ] 2 Chicken drumsticks
- [ ] A Bow and mushroom
- [ ] 3 Sodas
- [ ] A Motor car

UNDERGROUND HUNTERS

- [ ] A Snake in a bottle
- [ ] A Bookworm
- [ ] 2 Snakes on the telephone
- [ ] A Yo-yo
- [ ] 2 Dragons
- [ ] A Snake in a turban
- [ ] A Tightrope walker
- [ ] A Snakey spear
- [ ] 2 Green matches
- [ ] A Snake wearing lipstick
- [ ] 4 Pairs of eyes
- [ ] 4 Musical instruments
- [ ] A Snake golf club

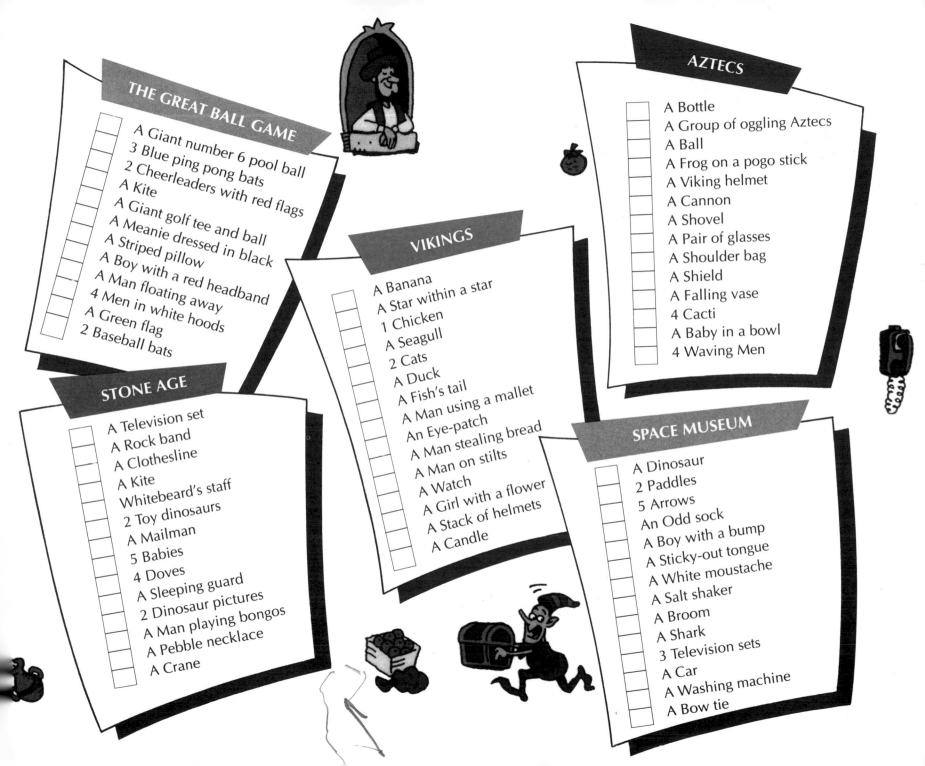

THE GREAT BALL GAME

- A Giant number 6 pool ball
- 3 Blue ping pong bats
- 2 Cheerleaders with red flags
- A Kite
- A Giant golf tee and ball
- A Meanie dressed in black
- A Striped pillow
- A Boy with a red headband
- A Man floating away
- 4 Men in white hoods
- A Green flag
- 2 Baseball bats

STONE AGE

- A Television set
- A Rock band
- A Clothesline
- A Kite
- Whitebeard's staff
- 2 Toy dinosaurs
- A Mailman
- 5 Babies
- 4 Doves
- A Sleeping guard
- 2 Dinosaur pictures
- A Man playing bongos
- A Pebble necklace
- A Crane

VIKINGS

- A Banana
- A Star within a star
- 1 Chicken
- A Seagull
- 2 Cats
- A Duck
- A Fish's tail
- A Man using a mallet
- An Eye-patch
- A Man stealing bread
- A Man on stilts
- A Watch
- A Girl with a flower
- A Stack of helmets
- A Candle

AZTECS

- A Bottle
- A Group of oggling Aztecs
- A Ball
- A Frog on a pogo stick
- A Viking helmet
- A Cannon
- A Shovel
- A Pair of glasses
- A Shoulder bag
- A Shield
- A Falling vase
- 4 Cacti
- A Baby in a bowl
- 4 Waving Men

SPACE MUSEUM

- A Dinosaur
- 2 Paddles
- 5 Arrows
- An Odd sock
- A Boy with a bump
- A Sticky-out tongue
- A White moustache
- A Salt shaker
- A Broom
- A Shark
- 3 Television sets
- A Car
- A Washing machine
- A Bow tie

DEEP SEA DIVERS:
The islands are: Newfoundland, Japan, Long Island, New Zealand, Cuba, British Isles, and Australia.

FLYING CARPETS:
The two identical heads of Blobi are: A and D.

DUNGEON:
Odlaw's Outlaws stole: a duck, a pipe, a soda, and a running vest.

UNDERGROUND HUNTERS:
Snake No. 2 is coming out of the basket.

STONE AGE:
The Chief Mushroom Mining Troll is searching for a spotted mushroom growing on the roof of a house.

GREAT BALL GAME:
The sportsman is equipped for: ping pong, football, cards, boxing, baseball, basketball, cricket, javelin, hockey, golf and scuba diving. The score of the Ball Game was: Bart's Hoods 9, Lou's Shorts 7.

AZTECS:
The number of blocks needed to rebuild the temple is: 21.

SPACE MUSEUM:
The scrambled planets should read: Pluto, Saturn, Jupiter, and Mercury.

The fun's not over yet Waldo Watchers! Have a look at the back cover. Each of the characters there appears once in our book sometimes even more. Can you spot them all, and find 13 scrolls?

WHERE IN WALDO'S WORLD AM I?

The "creature" below is made up of 1 element from each of the large scenes in this book. Can you find from which scene each piece comes from? Happy Hunting!